# THE TREAT TRUCK SERIES

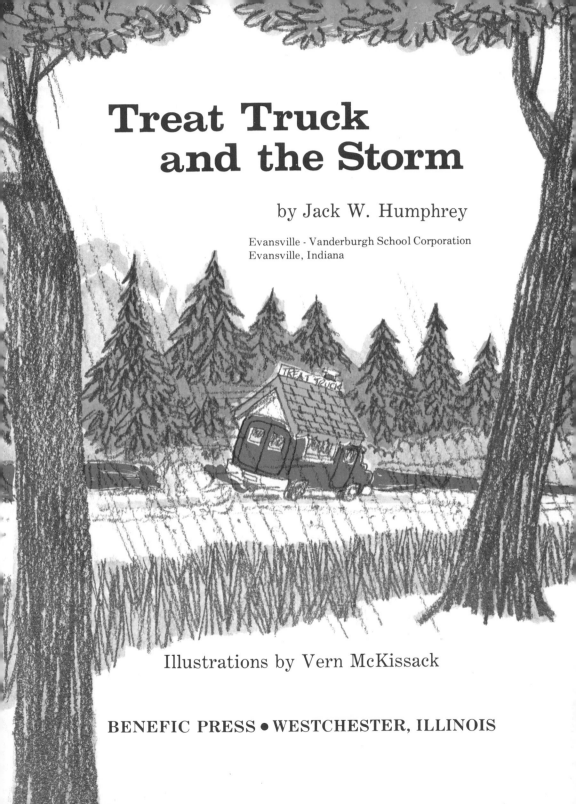

# Treat Truck
# and the Storm

### by Jack W. Humphrey

Evansville - Vanderburgh School Corporation
Evansville, Indiana

### Illustrations by Vern McKissack

**BENEFIC PRESS • WESTCHESTER, ILLINOIS**

ISBN 8175-2057-0

# Contents

# Jeff's Surprise

Mike was in the Treat Truck.

He was going to the school.

The sun was shining. It was a good day.

Mike got out of the truck.

He knew the children would want some treats.

"Mike is here!" said Andy.
"I want a treat," said Mary.
The children ran to the truck.
They wanted some ice cream. They
wanted some candy, too.

"Guess where we are going, Mike,"
said Andy.

"Back to school," said Mike.

"No," said Andy. "We are going on
a field trip. We are going to hike in
the forest."

"That will be fun," said Mike.

Jeff was standing behind Mike.
He had a horn. He blew on the horn.
OOGA! OOGA!
Mike jumped. He jumped very fast.
He jumped higher than the
Treat Truck.

"Was that a fire truck?" said Mike.

Then Mike saw the horn. He saw
Jeff, too.

Mike smiled. Then he laughed.

11

"What kind of horn is that?" said Mike. "It makes a loud noise."

"It is a circus horn," said Jeff. "It is used to call the animals."

"It is a good horn," said Mike. "It is good and loud."

Mrs. Schultz, the teacher, came to the Treat Truck.

"It is time to go on the field trip," she said.

"Good-by, Mike," said the children.

"Good-by," said Mike. "Have a good time."

# Can Mike Help?

Mike was busy.

Many people were hungry.

They came to the Treat Truck.

Frank and Fred came to the Treat Truck.

They had worked all morning.

They were very hungry.

Mike gave them some treats.

"Look at that!" said Frank.

"It looks bad," said Fred. "We can not work. It is going to rain."

They ate their treats.

Frank and Fred ate hot dogs. Mike had one, too.

16

Mr. Brown, the principal, ran out of the school. He saw Mike.

"Mike," he said. "There is bad news. A big storm is coming."

"The children are in school," said Fred. "They will be safe."

17

"They will be safe," said Mr. Brown. "But some of the children went on a field trip. They are in the forest. They will not be safe."

"That is bad," said Fred.

"They can not walk in a storm," said Mr. Brown. "Some one must go find them."

"I will find them," said Mike.

"We must take the food out of the truck. Then the children can fit in it."

Every one went to the Treat Truck. They took the food and put it in the school.

Mike ran to the truck and got in. "I will find the children," he said.

## Mike Goes to the Forest

There were many cars and trucks on the road. Mike could not go fast. Mike found a side road. There were not so many cars. He could go faster.

Mike was going fast.

There was a truck with chickens in front of the Treat Truck.

Mike just missed the truck.

Some of the chickens fell off the truck. There were chickens everywhere.

Mike turned.

Something hit his side. Mike picked it up. It was Jeff's horn. He had left the horn in the truck.

The sky got darker and darker.

Mike could not see. He could not go fast.

Mike got to the forest.

He got out of the truck. Then he looked for the children.

"Mrs. Schultz! Jeff! Any one!" he called.

There was not a sound.

Mike was scared. He did not know what to do.

Where could the children be?

Mike walked back to the truck.

He opened the door.

Jeff's horn fell out of the truck.

# What Does Mike Do?

Mike picked up the horn. He blew on the horn. It did not make any noise.

Mike said, "Jeff could blow the horn. I can, too."

He tried again. There still was no noise.

Mike shook the horn. An egg fell out. Would it work now?

Mike tried again.

OOGA! OOGA!

"It works!" said Mike. "May be the children will hear it."

Mike was happy. He blew on the horn again.

OOGA! OOGA! He wanted all the children to hear it.

Mike put the horn down. He waited for the children to come.

Then Mike heard a noise. "That must be the children," he said.

He picked up the horn and ran into the forest.

Mike walked far into the forest and stopped.

He heard the noise again.

Some deer ran by Mike. They had made the noise.

Mike still did not know where the children were.

# Is Every One Safe?

Mike walked farther into the forest.
The storm was coming nearer.
He had to make the children hear the horn.
He blew as hard as he could.
OOGA! OOGA!
Mike heard something. It sounded like some one was calling his name.
He thought it was the children.

Mike blew the horn again.
OOGA! OOGA!
Then he heard more voices.

Mrs. Schultz and the children heard
Mike's horn. They had found him.
Every one was happy to see Mike.
Mike was happy, too.

Mike led the children back to the Treat Truck. The storm began.

The children and Mrs. Schultz hurried into the truck.

Mike got into the truck, too.

# Jeff's Treat

Mike started the Treat Truck. He drove slowly. The road was bad.

A big tree fell down. It fell in front of the Treat Truck.

They could not go any where.

What would they do now?

Mike backed up the truck. It went
into the mud. The Treat Truck still
could not go.

40

Mike got the truck back on the
road. Soon they were out of
the forest.

Mike got to the school. The storm had stopped. The sun came out.

Mr. Brown saw the Treat Truck. He ran out of the school.

"Is every one safe?" he said.

"I think so," said Mike. "But we had a bad ride."

The children got out of the truck.
They were happy to be back at school.
Every one talked at once.

Mike blew the horn again. Then every one was quiet.

Jeff said, "Thank you, Mike. You saved us."

"Thank you, Mike," said Mr. Brown.

The children clapped their hands.

"I want you to keep the horn," said Jeff. "Then you can help others, too."

Then Jeff came up behind Mike. He blew the horn.

OOGA! OOGA!

Mike jumped into the air. Every one laughed and laughed.

Mike said, "I am glad Jeff gave me the horn. I could not stand any more surprises."

# Vocabulary

The total vocabulary of this book is 199 words, excluding proper names and sound words. Of these, 178 words are below second-grade level and are not listed. Endings *s*, *es*, *d*, *ed*, and *ing* are assumed known additions to root words and these forms are not listed separately. The fifteen words shown in roman type are familiar to children reading on a second-grade level. The six words above second-grade level are shown in italic type. The number indicates the page on which the word first appears.

| | | |
|---|---|---|
| bad 16 | hit 23 | *principal* 17 |
| *blew* 10 | horn 10 | |
| busy 15 | | safe 19 |
| | ice cream 8 | *scared* 25 |
| deer 31 | | shook 28 |
| | loud 13 | sound 25 |
| *fit* 19 | | storm 17 |
| | miss(ed) 22 | |
| forest 9 | | *Treat* 7 |
| | news 17 | trip 9 |
| *hike* 9 | | |

## Names and Sound Words

| | | |
|---|---|---|
| Andy 8 | Jeff 10 | Mr. Brown 17 |
| Frank 15 | Mary 8 | Mrs. Schultz 13 |
| Fred 15 | Mike 7 | ooga 10 |